The Pet

Kasia Reay

Illustrated by Farah Shah

Schofield & Sims

Ro<u>ss</u> an<u>d</u> his da<u>d</u> met a pet...

but did Ro<u>ss</u> get the pet?

Ro<u>ss</u> and his dad fed a pet...

but did Ro<u>ss</u> get the pet?

Ro<u>ss</u> and his da<u>d</u> led a pet...

but did Ro<u>ss</u> get the pet?

No, Ro<u>ss</u> got Ned the Ted!